BUMPER ACTIVITY BOOK

This bumper book is full of alien activities! Use the awesome stickers to complete the puzzles and creepy scenes.

EGMONT

We bring stories to life

First published in Great Britain 2010 by Egmont UK Limited
239 Kensington High Street, London W8 6SA

Cartoon Network, the logo, BEN 10 Alien Force and all related characters
and elements are trademarks of and © 2010 Cartoon Network.
(s10)

ISBN 978 1 4052 4998 0
1 3 5 7 9 10 8 6 4 2
Printed in China

MEET THE ALIENS!

Ben Tennyson is back and this time he has more villains to conquer than ever before! If he is going to save the world, he is going to need to call on his new alien forms.

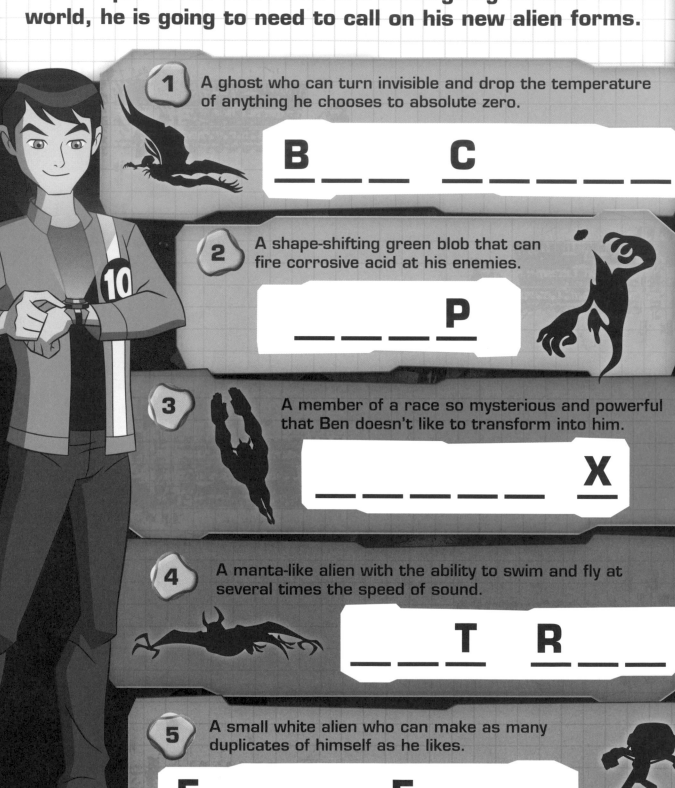

1 A ghost who can turn invisible and drop the temperature of anything he chooses to absolute zero.

B _ _ _ C _ _ _ _ _ _

2 A shape-shifting green blob that can fire corrosive acid at his enemies.

_ _ _ _ _ P

3 A member of a race so mysterious and powerful that Ben doesn't like to transform into him.

_ _ _ _ _ _ _ X

4 A manta-like alien with the ability to swim and fly at several times the speed of sound.

_ _ _ T R _ _ _

5 A small white alien who can make as many duplicates of himself as he likes.

E _ _ _ _ E _ _ _ _ _

Work out who each alien fact is describing, then place the matching alien stickers over the black shadows.

You'd better be quick – you never know when the Omnitrix is going to call on them!

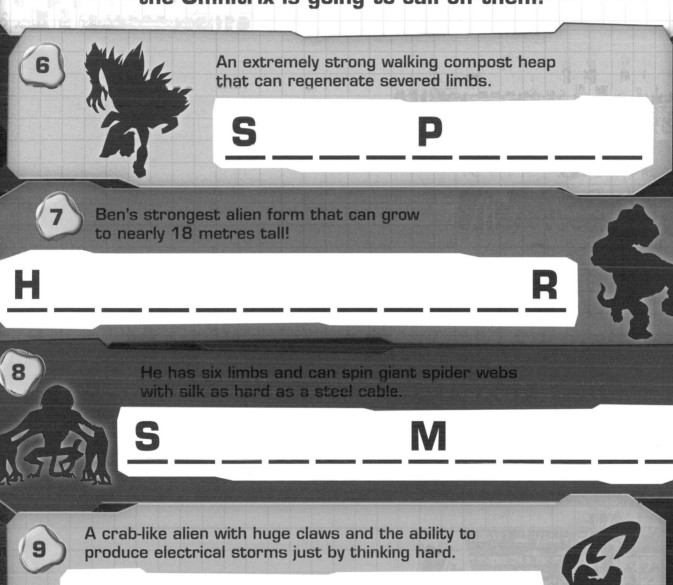

6 An extremely strong walking compost heap that can regenerate severed limbs.

S _ _ _ _ P _ _ _ _ _

7 Ben's strongest alien form that can grow to nearly 18 metres tall!

H _ _ _ _ _ _ _ _ _ _ _ _ _ _ R

8 He has six limbs and can spin giant spider webs with silk as hard as a steel cable.

S _ _ _ _ _ _ _ M _ _ _ _ _

9 A crab-like alien with huge claws and the ability to produce electrical storms just by thinking hard.

B _ _ _ _ _ _ _ _ _ _ _ M

10 A living crystal that can absorb energy and channel it into blasts.

C _ _ _ _ _ _ S _ _ _ _

Answers: 1. Big Chill, 2. Goop, 3. Alien X, 4. Jet Ray, 5. Echo Echo, 6. Swampfire, 7. Humungousaur, 8. Spidermonkey, 9. Brainstorm, 10. Chromastone.

3

MAGIC POWERS

Gwen has been practising her own superpowers.
She can control energy and is able to form
magical orbs, shields and platforms!

Find two images of Gwen in combat
that are exactly the same.

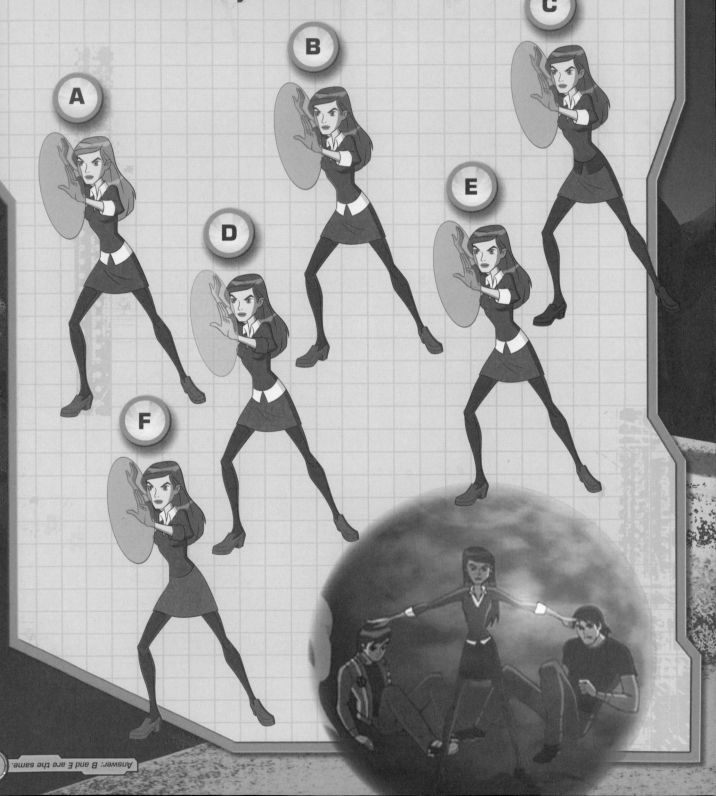

MAX'S WARNING

Grandpa Max has left Ben an important message. But Ben is having trouble deciphering the code.

Can you work it out? Follow the circle in a clockwise direction starting at the top, and write every third letter in the space below.

_____ ___ ____

___ _____

_____ _____.

GOOP CHALLENGE

Goop can take on many slimy shapes. How many images of our gunky friend can you count?

Answer: 30 images of Goop.

ARCTIC GRID!

With his icy breath blast, Big Chill can drop the temperature of anything he chooses to freezing point! But can you fit these icy words into the frosty grid below? Big Chill has done three for you . . .

3 LETTERS
ICE
RAW

4 LETTERS
COOL
HAIL
NUMB
SNOW

5 LETTERS
SHARP
~~STORM~~
CHILL
FROST
POLAR

6 LETTERS
ICICLE
SHIVER
~~ARCTIC~~
BITTER

7 LETTERS
~~GLACIAL~~

DNALiEN ATTACK!

The DNAliens are an evil threat to planet Earth. It's important that Ben can recognise them from afar.

Only one of these figures is the real deal. The rest are fakes. The true DNAlien will look slightly different to all of the rest. Can you help Ben work it out?

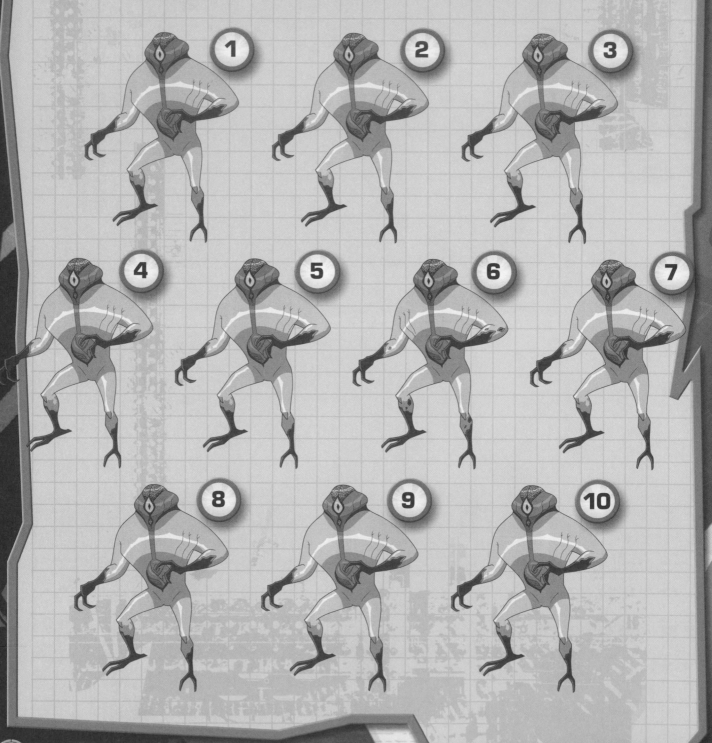

Answer: number 6 is the real DNAlien. The imposters have markings and gills missing.

ALiEN COMBAT!

The battle is on!
Follow the burning fireballs to find out
who is fighting who.

RESCUE MISSION

The DNAliens have captured Gwen! They've sprayed poisonous gases into the air so Kevin E. Levin can't find his way. Can you show him the path to Gwen before it's too late?

Beware! Choose the wrong path and Kevin could collide with one of the evil villains.

ALIEN CHECK

Which close-ups belong to which of Ben's aliens?
Write your answers in the panels below.

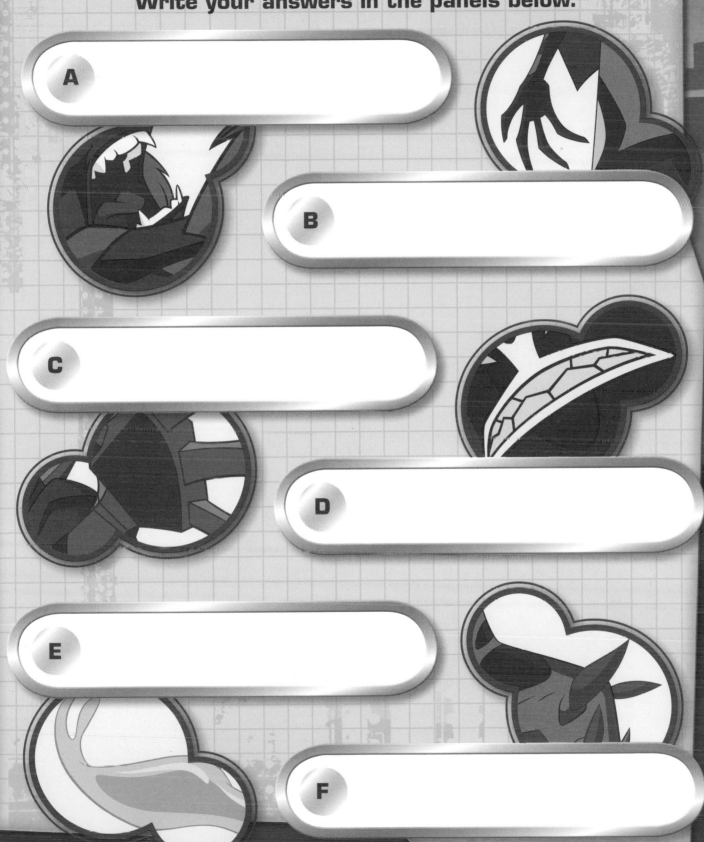

A

B

C

D

E

F

Answers: A – Spidermonkey, B – Big Chill, C – ChromoStone, D – Jet Ray, E – Goop, F – Swampfire.

SECRET WEB

Can you find your way through Spidermonkey's web?
When you have, collect all of the letters that the route
passes. The letters should spell out one of Ben's most
annoying high school enemies!

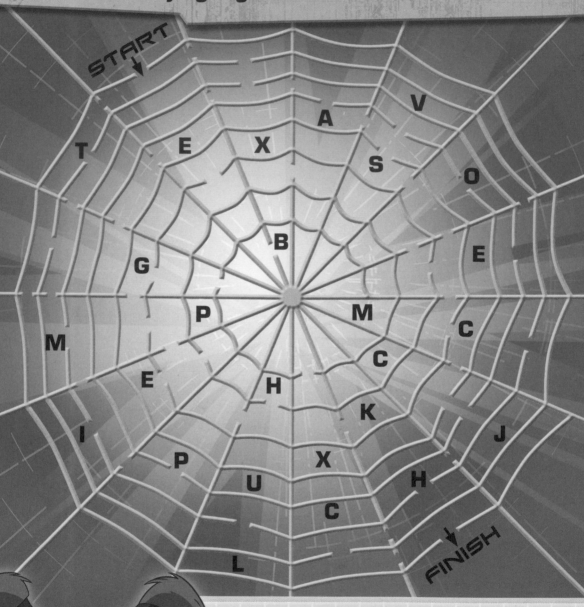

START

V
A
T
E
X
S
O
B
E
G
P
M
M
C
C
E
H
I
K
J
P
X
H
U
C
L
FINISH

Letters picked up along the way:

___ ___ ___ ___ ___ ___

Ben's arch enemy is:

___ ___ ___ ___ ___

EVIL TRADE

The Forever Knights are part of a top-secret organisation. Can you crack the code to work out what it is they are hiding?

A	B	C	D	E	F
1	2	3	4	5	6

G	H	I	J	K	L	M
7	8	9	10	11	12	13

N	O	P	Q	R	S	T	U
14	15	16	17	18	19	20	21

V	W	X	Y	Z
22	23	24	25	26

20	8	5	25

19	5	12	12

1	14	4

21	19	5

4	1	14	7	5	18	15	21	19

1	12	9	5	14

23	5	1	16	15	14	19

DOUBLE VISION

Swampfire has projected holographic images of himself on to the cave walls to confuse the villains. Can you work out which two images are a matching pair?

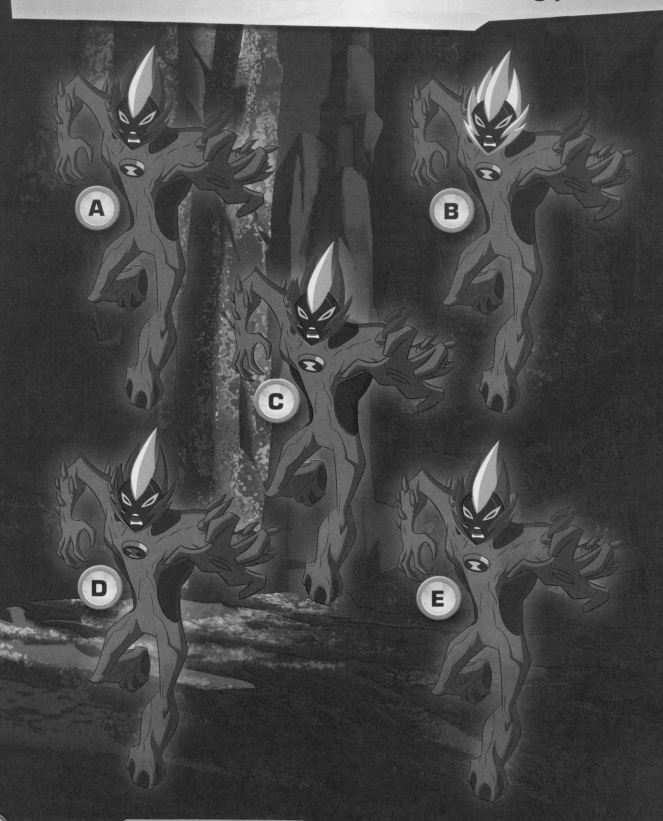

Answer: A and E are the same. B has yellow flames around his head; C has red markings on his head; D has green flames on his shoulders and a red Omnitrix.

MEMORY TEST

It's time to test your brainpower.

Study this image of the Forever Knights with their evil leader, Patrick. Then cover it up and take the test.

1. How many knights are visible in the 1st row? _____

2. What are the knights holding in their hands? _____

3. What colour is Patrick's cloak? _____

4. Does Patrick have a moustache? _____

5. What is Patrick wearing on his head? _____

JET RAY PUZZLE

Jet Ray is a manta-like creature that can fly through the air faster than the speed of sound.

Identify the missing pieces of this scene of Jet Ray in action. Then find the matching stickers to complete the puzzle!

Answers: 1-F, 2-A, 3-D, 4-G

MULTIPLICITY

How many times does Echo Echo appear in the box below?

PROGRAMME: DUPLICATE

Echo Echo can duplicate himself into a limitless number of exact replicas. Can you draw an exact replica of him? Copy his form into the grid. It will be easier if you copy it square by square.

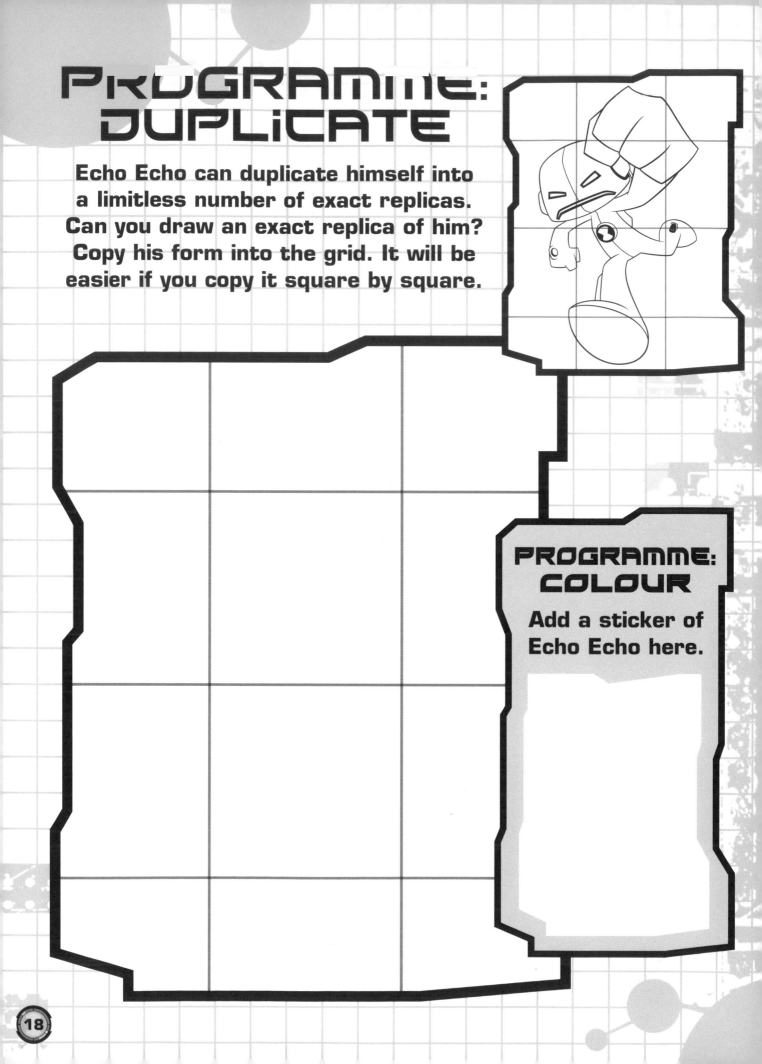

PROGRAMME: COLOUR

Add a sticker of Echo Echo here.

CHROMA-SEARCH

When you've conquered this wordsearch, look at the 10th row and write down all the unused letters. Then unscramble them to reveal something that ChromaStone uses in battle!

Swampfire	ChromaStone	Brainstorm	Jet Ray
Big Chill	Ben	Max	Alien X
Goop	Kevin	Gwen	

S	A	B	I	G	C	H	I	L	L	R	S
A	W	M	T	E	N	R	O	P	T	B	T
L	P	A	E	C	H	V	G	O	O	P	E
I	L	X	M	N	S	B	W	U	B	E	M
N	M	W	N	P	R	H	E	O	S	L	O
E	C	A	B	B	F	A	N	L	R	R	L
B	H	S	L	L	R	I	S	A	P	E	P
X	R	T	O	I	A	L	R	J	I	U	J
B	O	A	P	L	E	X	R	E	G	S	B
L	M	A	I	S	E	N	R	T	W	S	E
F	A	L	E	N	E	S	X	R	E	W	N
G	S	D	R	V	S	L	I	A	N	Q	I
W	T	F	R	B	R	T	N	Y	R	R	E
D	O	S	F	N	J	B	O	S	T	N	N
T	N	E	K	E	V	I	N	R	N	E	X
M	E	R	S	A	N	P	O	V	M	P	P

Collected letters:

ChromaStone uses _____ to fight with!

SLIME ATTACK!

Read this awesome comic strip and draw pictures to match each scene. Use your stickers to help you!

A mutant slime is covering the skyscrapers of Washington DC!

Ben uses the Omnitrix to transform into Big Chill!

Gwen is trapped in the powerful slime!

Big Chill blows icy air at the slime. The slime freezes and Gwen is safe. For now . . .

ECHO DUPLICATION

Echo Echo has duplicated his name horizontally in the grid below. How many times can you see his full name? Write your answer in the blank box.

E	C	H	P	E	C	H	O	E	C	H	O
E	H	C	O	E	C	H	O	E	H	C	O
E	C	H	O	E	C	H	O	E	O	H	O
E	H	C	O	E	C	H	O	E	H	C	O
E	C	H	O	E	C	H	O	E	C	H	E
C	H	O	E	C	H	O	E	C	H	O	E
C	H	E	C	H	O	E	C	H	O	E	E
O	H	E	C	H	O	E	H	C	O	E	C
O	O	E	C	H	E	C	H	O	O	E	H
C	O	E	C	H	O	E	C	H	O	E	H
C	O	E	C	H	O	E	C	H	E	C	O
E	E	C	H	O	E	C	H	O	E	C	H

ALIEN POWER

Create your own super alien and draw it in the space below. Remember to give it a name and to think up 3 awesome alien facts!

NAME: _____

SUPERPOWER: _____

STRENGTHS: _____

WEAKNESSES: _____

OMNITRIX MIX-UP

The Omnitrix is malfunctioning. Unscramble the names below so Ben can kick some serious alien butt!

When you've worked them out, find the alien stickers so the Omnitrix is ready for action.

1

Y A J
R T E

_ _ _ _ _ _

2

B C I L
G I H L

_ _ _ _ _ _

T B M O I
N A R R S

3

_ _ _ _ _ _ _ _ _ _

4

A
M W P R E S F I

_ _ _ _ _ _ _ _ _

DRAW GOOP!

Study this picture of Goop. Then draw over the lines to create your own Goop!

EVIL MESSAGE

**The HighBreed are Ben's most powerful enemy.
They are believed to be the first intelligent life forms ever!
But what do they want with planet Earth?**

A	B	C	D	E	F	G	H	I	J	K	L	M
1	2	3	4	5	6	7	8	9	10	11	12	13

N	O	P	Q	R	S	T	U	V	W	X	Y	Z
14	15	16	17	18	19	20	21	22	23	24	25	26

Row 1: 20 8 5 25 __ 23 1 14 20 __ 20 15

Row 2: 3 12 5 1 14 19 5 __ 20 8 5

Row 3: 21 14 9 22 5 18 19 5 __ 15 6

Row 4: 1 12 12 __ 18 1 3 5 19 __ 2 21 20

Row 5: 20 8 5 13 19 5 12 22 5 19

ViLLAiN ALERT

The HighBreed, DNAliens and the Forever Knights are a massive threat to planet Earth. Think up a new evil villain and draw it in the space below.

NAME: _____

SUPERPOWER: _____

EVIL THREAT: _____

MOONLIGHT SHADOWS

Which shadow belongs to which alien? The shadows are in different poses to confuse you!

Answers: 1 - B, 2 - A, 3 - E, 4 - D, 5 - C.

TAKE THE TEST

The time has come to test your alien knowledge.
How well do you know the secrets of the force?
Pass the test and you're in the game!
Fail and you still have a lot to learn.

1 Who owns a car?

a) Gwen
b) Ben
c) Kevin

2 Which alien can turn invisible?

a) Swampfire
b) Big Chill
c) Echo Echo

3 Who are the loyal servants to the HighBreed?

a) DNAliens
b) The Forever Knights
c) Alien X and ChromaStone

4 What is Kevin's superpower?

a) he can absorb metal, wood and stone
b) he can fly
c) he can morph into a dragon

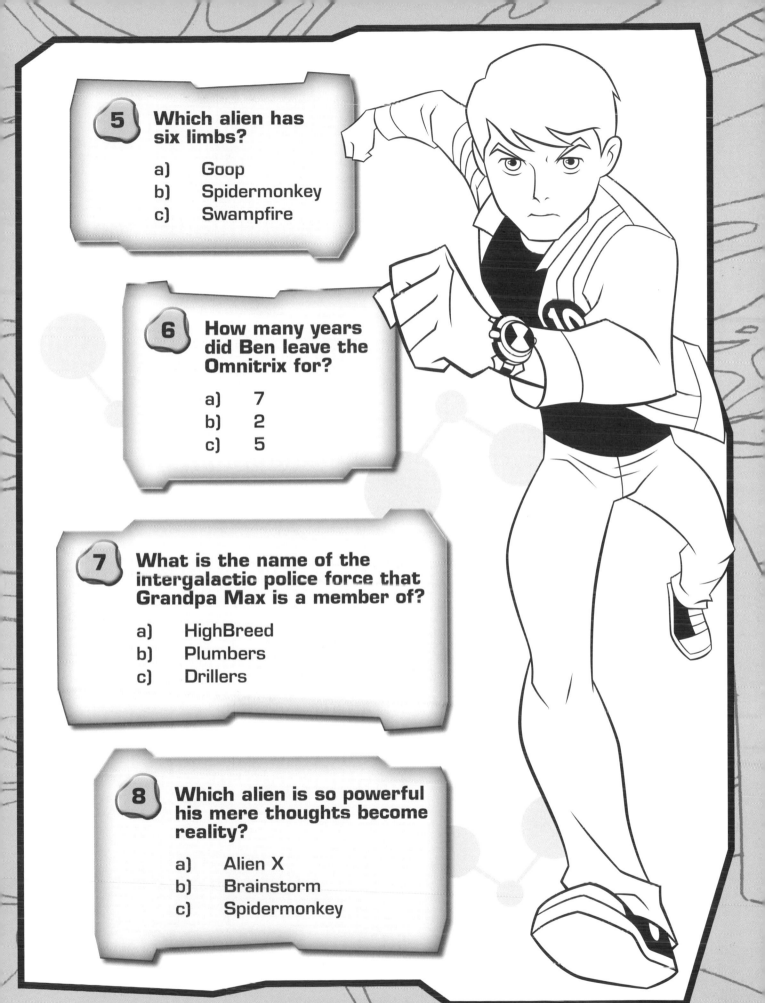

5 Which alien has six limbs?

a) Goop
b) Spidermonkey
c) Swampfire

6 How many years did Ben leave the Omnitrix for?

a) 7
b) 2
c) 5

7 What is the name of the intergalactic police force that Grandpa Max is a member of?

a) HighBreed
b) Plumbers
c) Drillers

8 Which alien is so powerful his mere thoughts become reality?

a) Alien X
b) Brainstorm
c) Spidermonkey

CASTLE TRAP!

Ben is trapped in the Forever Knights' castle and the lights have gone out! Luckily, he has got a torch to shine a route out of there.

Use a black pen or felt tip to scribble over all the squares with □ or ◙. Then follow the squares with ⠿ and ○ to find the way out!

START

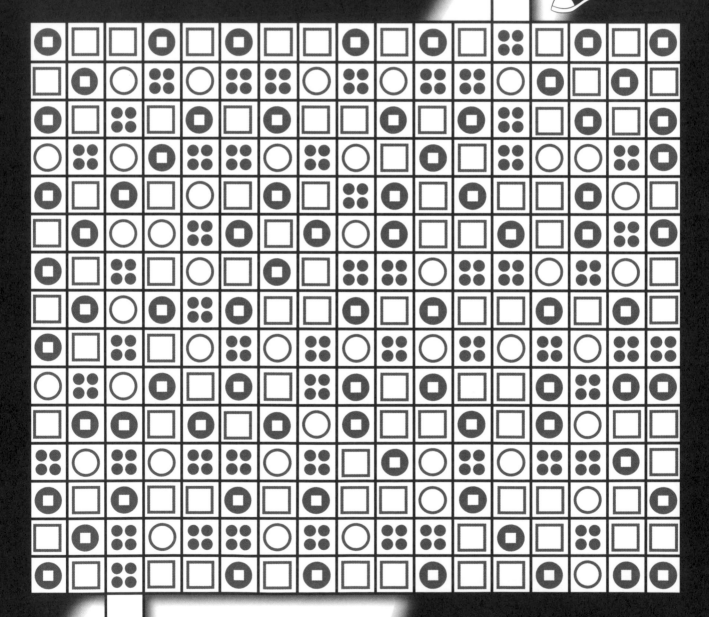

FINISH

CHROMASTONE CHECK OUT

One of these pictures of ChromaStone is a fake.
It will look different to the rest. Can you spot it?

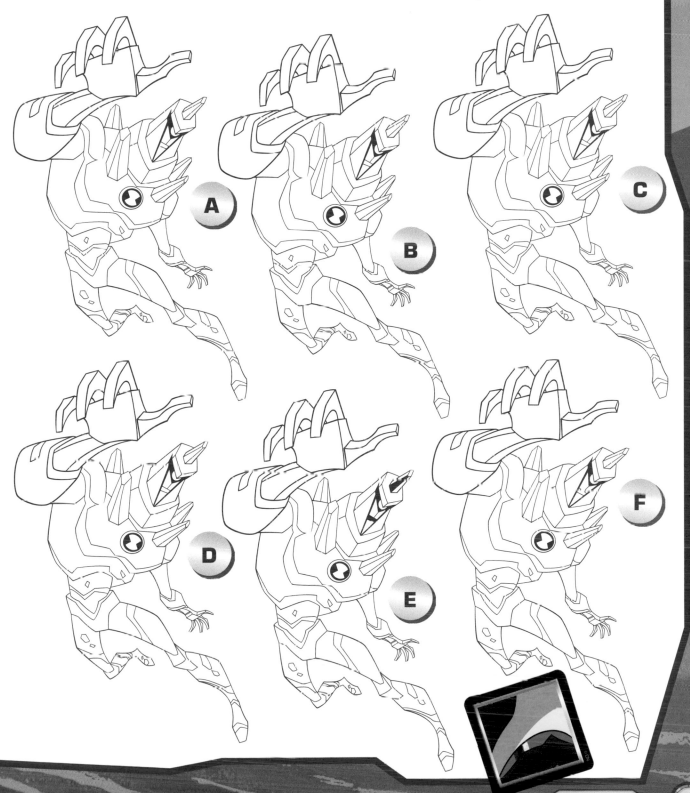

MORNINGSTAR MESSAGE

Kevin has overheard the evil villain, Mike Morningstar, having a conversation. He needs to get a message to Ben urgently! Can you unscramble the tiles to find out what Mike Morningstar is up to?

| TO | HAS | THE |

| POWER | LIFE | DRAIN |

| MORNINGSTAR | FROM |

| THE | MIKE | PEOPLE |

HINT: The first tile is 'MIKE'

MiND BENDER

Study this scene for **10 seconds**. Then cover it up.
Test your memory by seeing how many of Jet Ray's
questions you can answer.

1. What colour are Gwen's magical orbs? _____

2. What species is the villain? _____

3. How many people are watching the action? _____

4. What is the villain doing? _____

5. Name 2 colours on the villain's head. _____

HEAT BUSTER

The villains are chasing Ben into the scorching desert. He'll need to turn the temperature right down if he's going to win this fight! Study your stickers and add the best alien for this battle. Add some more villains, too!

GWEN'S WARNING

Gwen is trying to send a message to Ben. Can you unleash your brainpower to add the correct letters and decipher the message?

T___
DN__L___N_
_R_ PL___T_NG
T_ __EST___Y
_R_N_P_ M_X

O T A G A
H E A I S
I E O A R
D A E D O

ALIEN DARKNESS

Only one of these shadows matches this image of Humungousaur. Which one is it?

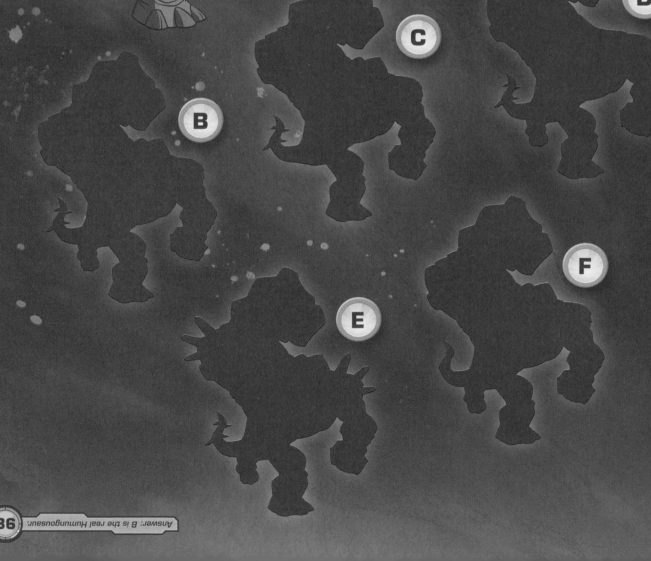

Answer: B is the real Humungousaur.

HiGHBREED CLOSE-UPS

Study the scene of this HighBreed and DNAlien.
Which close-up has been taken from the main picture?

GLOOPY MAZE!

Goop has created a gooey maze to protect Gwen from a **DNAlien** attack – but there are ways to get through! You can block off three paths by colouring in the points marked ⬙. Which three paths must you block off to protect Gwen?

ALIEN DETECTOR

Look at this picture of Ben. Can you work out which alien is going to appear? Ben's speech might help you decide.

Come on, you stupid watch! DNAliens are coming! I need something with some serious brain power if we're gonna survive!

1

2

3

LASER BLAST-OFF!

The DNAliens are trying to use mirrors to blast Kevin and Gwen! Which DNAlien's beam should Ben block to stop Kevin and Gwen getting fired at?

Lasers bounce off mirrors like this:

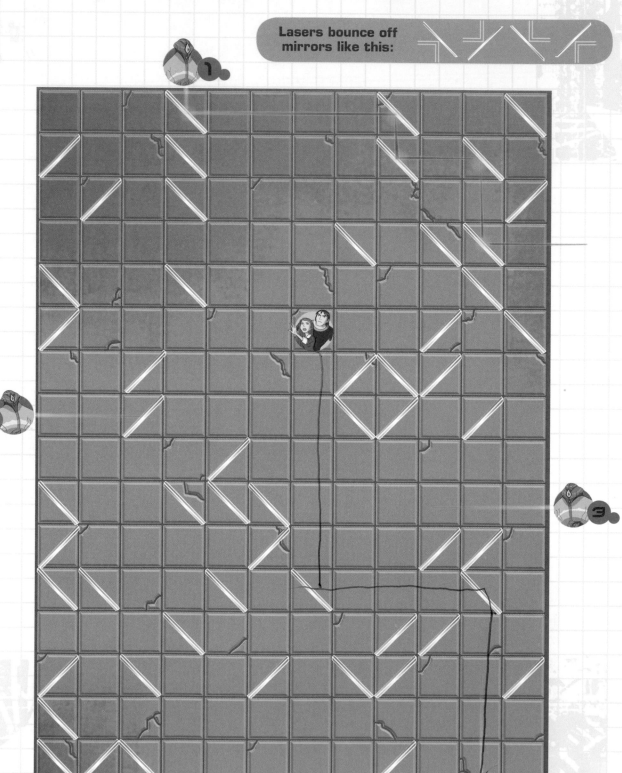

PSYCHIC POWERS

Do you have the power to predict the Omnitrix?
Quickly read the descriptions of the three scenes below.
Which alien will the Omnitrix choose for which battle?
Write your answers in the Omnitrix panels. Good luck!

The Forever Knights are having a secret meeting in their castle. Ben needs to find out what deadly plans they are cooking up. He will need to make himself invisible if he is going to slip in unnoticed!

1   BEN NEEDS ...

If Ben is going to beat this evil rat, he is going to need to make some high-pitched sonic waves to throw the rat off the scent.

2   BEN NEEDS ...

This huge dragon is super strong. Ben is going to need awesome physical strength and power if he is going to defeat this beast!

3   BEN NEEDS ...

KNiGHT MATCH

Find the two Forever Knights that
are exact copies of each other.

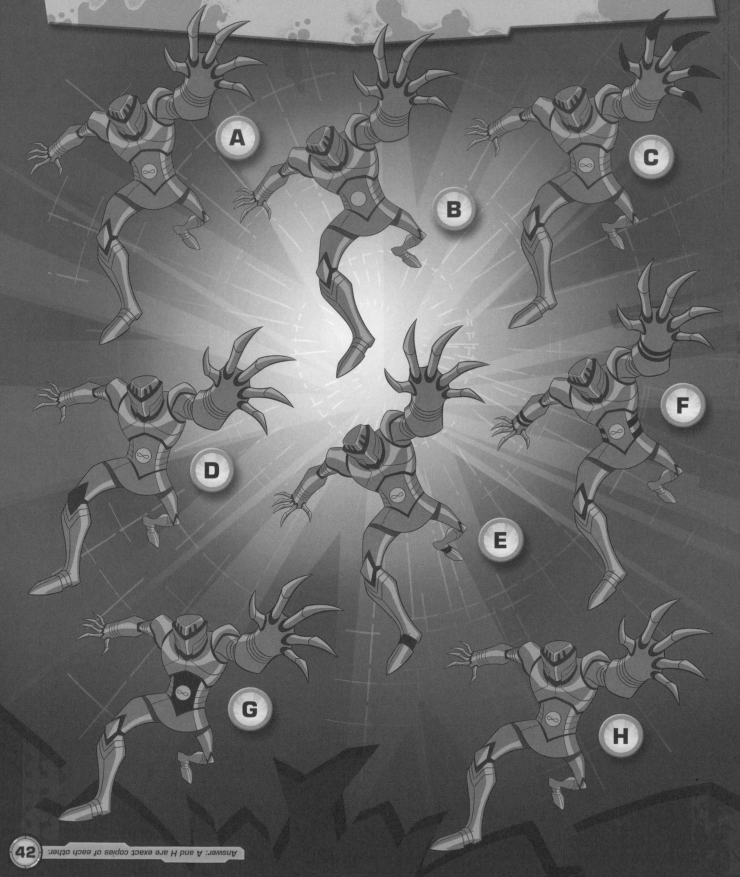

Answer: A and H are exact copies of each other.

HiGHBREED ATTACK

How many HighBreed can you count?
Write your answer in the blank box.

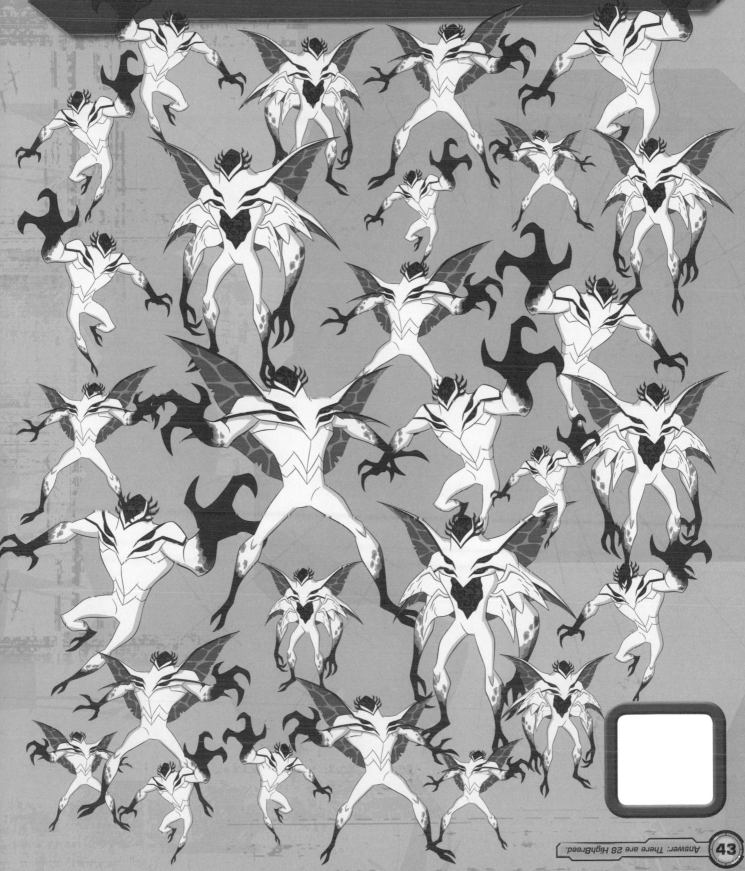

BATTLE SCENE

Use your stickers to create an all-out battle scene between Ben, Kevin and the sinister villains! Who wins? Only you can decide . . .

VULKANUS VS KEVIN E. LEVIN

The evil Vulkanus wants revenge on Kevin for a past betrayal. Kevin needs some ammunition. And fast! Help him through the maze to his car so he can pick up his own deadly supplies!

START →

FINISH →

ZOMBIE THREAT

Mike Morningstar is on the rampage! He's running through Washington DC turning people into zombies. It's up to you to stop him. But first, you have to find him!

Find a friend to play with and see who can reach Mike Morningstar first. But you'd better be quick, the world is in serious danger!

ALIEN CHALLENGE
Which alien can shoot flames?

ZOMBIE ALERT!

START

TO SAVE THE WORLD, YOU WILL NEED:

- a friend to play with

- a dice

- some coins or counters. You could use the stickers in this book to make counters

- you may need 2 heavy objects to weigh the pages down!

RULE CHECK:

- if you land on an image of a zombie, go back 5 places

- if you land on an image of Brainstorm, go forward 3 places

- if you land on an image of Gwen, go forward 2 places

- if you land on an alien challenge, complete it successfully or go back to the start!

ZOMBIE ALERT!

ALIEN CHALLENGE
Which alien can spin webs?

ALIEN CHALLENGE
Which alien can drop the temperature to zero?

ZOMBIE ALERT!

FINISH

DESTRUCTION

The Forever Knights have some seriously deadly alien weapons. They are not afraid to cause mass destruction on earth.

Find 5 differences between these images before they open fire on you!

Check your answers on pages 62–63

DRAW HUMUNGOUSAUR

Draw over the grey lines to create your own Humungousaur!

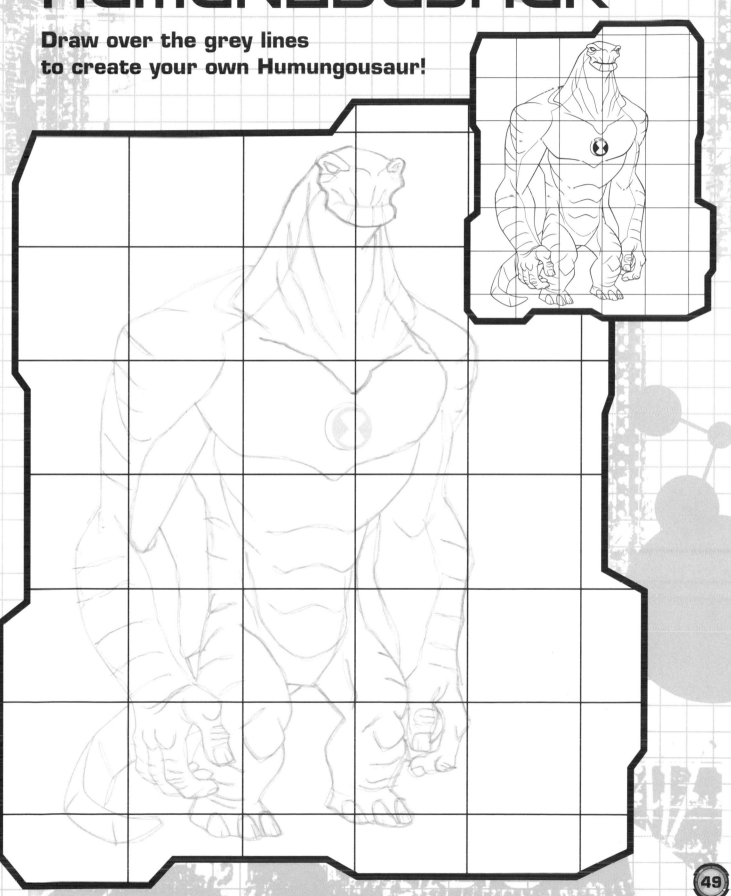

SQUARE OFF

The battle is on! You will need someone to challenge in this battle of concentration. Take turns drawing a straight line between any two black dots. If the line you draw completes a square, put your initials in it and take another shot. When all the dots have been connected, the player with most points wins!

SCORES: Player 1: _____ points.   Player 2: _____ points.

SHADOW MATCH

Can you work out which shadow belongs to which villain?
The shadows are in different poses to confuse you!

WORD EXPLOSION

Make as many words as you can using the letters below.
There are two done already to get you started.

ALIEN SUPERPOWERS

surprise

weapon

COSMIC SEARCH

Can you find these evil words in the grid below?
Words can read up, down, across and diagonally.

Forever Knights **Evil** **Weapons**
Ammunition **Galaxy** **Destroy**
HighBreed **Villains** **Armour**
DNAliens **Zombies** **Battle**

Y X H I G H B R E E D S Y T F
O S Z B A C F W V S N D S D O
R T Y N L B Y B I W A C X Z R
T Y K X A Q F M L C L K H B E
S C V W X Z S X Q Z I N D K V
E W G R Y F B U J Z E C Y B E
D S E Q W K V D A P N C Z J R
W X T A B P J R T K S F B S K
F C Q V P A M M U N I T I O N
Z X D W Q O T S D K B V X K I
R F S K U L N T V S Y W Z D G
Y M P R F C R S L B X D C L H
X T K B D Y K S F E L G T J T
Z O M B I E S V I L L A I N S

NUMBER RESCUE

The DNAliens are descending and Gwen's magical orbs are failing. Can you show Kevin the quickest path to Gwen before it's too late? The quickest path is the route with the smallest total when the numbers are added together.

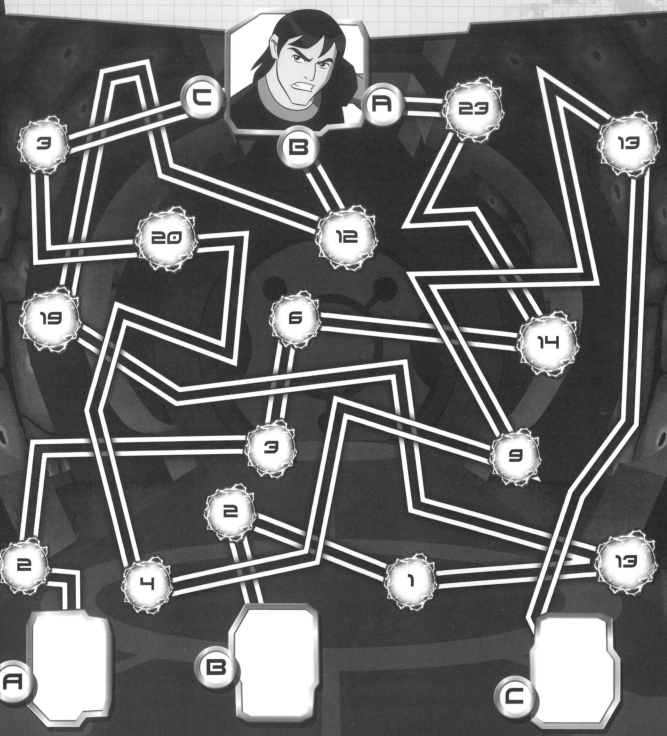

When you've worked it out, find a sticker of Gwen and stick at the end of the correct line.

LASER PUZZLE

ChromaStone is playing with his lasers – parts of him have disappeared! Can you work out which pieces are missing?

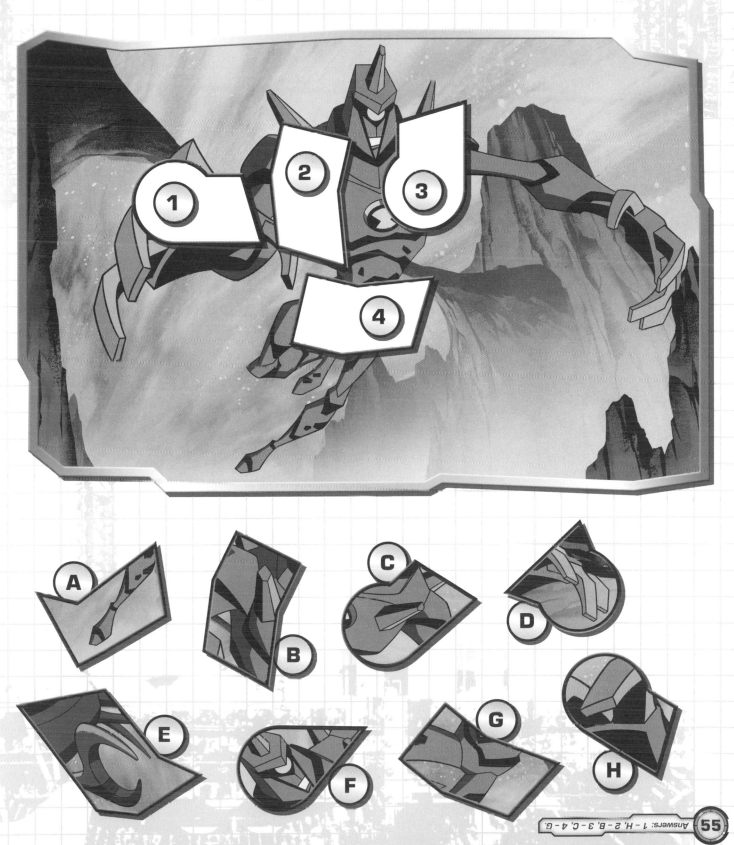

DESIGN ALIEN TECH

Alien technology is getting more and more advanced. Can you design your own awesome piece of alien ammunition to help Ben kick some serious butt?

AMMUNITION NAME: _____

WHAT IT DOES: _____

_____

FIND THE OBJECT

Ben has kept something hidden for 5 years.
Cross out all the letters that appear more than once.
Then rearrange the letters that are left to reveal the
word. 2 letters have already been done for you.

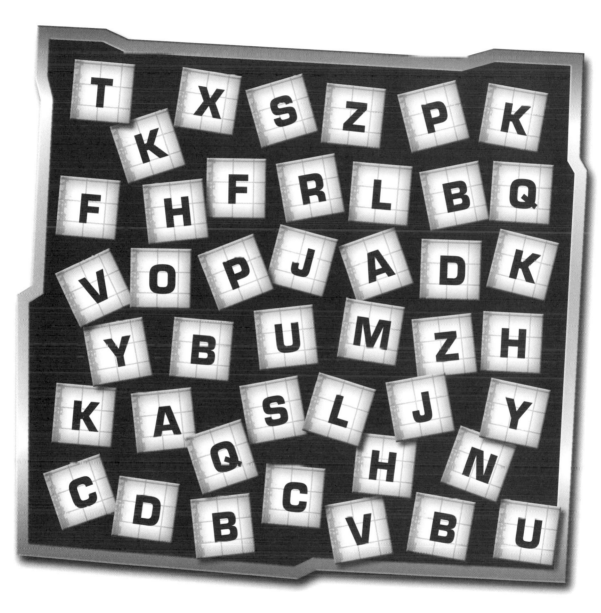

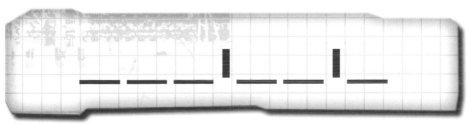

_ _ _ _ I _ I _

ALiEN BLAST

This bad guy means trouble. Blast him with the fiery stickers! You could colour him in, too.

CYBER GRID

Study this grid. The car, the Omnitrix, Alien X and Goop should appear once in each column, row and mini grid. Draw or write the names of the aliens and objects in the blank squares.

ALIEN X CHALLENGE

Alien X is a member of a race so powerful that Ben doesn't like to transform into him. He can alter space and time. Alien X is hiding somewhere in this book.

It's time to turn back time and go and find him!

Unravel the clues to find out where Ben's mysterious alien is hiding. Start by turning backwards to page 15 . . .

1 You're back in the castle of the Forever Knights. Count how many black lines you can see on evil Patrick's left arm. Be quick – you don't want to be seen!
Now turn back 2 pages . . .

2 In the code which number is used for the first initial of Ben's cousin's name? And just to make it a little more tricky, multiply that number by 2.
Now turn forwards 16 pages . . .

3 This one should be easy to collect! Just take the answer to the 6th question. Got it? Now for the final number.
Now turn forwards 14 pages . . .

4 How many HighBreed did you count? Zap 5 of them with your blast stickers. How many are there now? You should now have all 4 numbers.
Now turn forwards 8 pages to find your first letter . . .

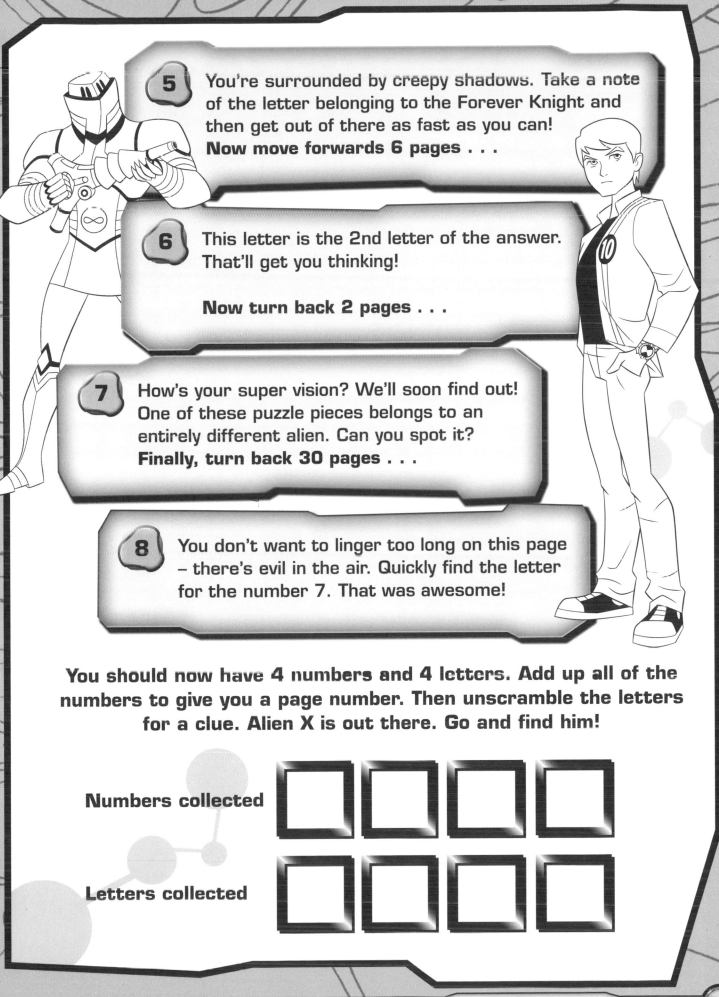

5 You're surrounded by creepy shadows. Take a note of the letter belonging to the Forever Knight and then get out of there as fast as you can! **Now move forwards 6 pages . . .**

6 This letter is the 2nd letter of the answer. That'll get you thinking!

Now turn back 2 pages . . .

7 How's your super vision? We'll soon find out! One of these puzzle pieces belongs to an entirely different alien. Can you spot it? **Finally, turn back 30 pages . . .**

8 You don't want to linger too long on this page – there's evil in the air. Quickly find the letter for the number 7. That was awesome!

You should now have **4 numbers** and **4 letters**. Add up all of the numbers to give you a page number. Then unscramble the letters for a clue. Alien X is out there. Go and find him!

Numbers collected

Letters collected

ANSWERS

P7 ARCTIC GRID!

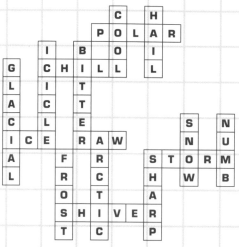

P10 RESCUE MISSION

P12 SECRET WEB

Ben's arch enemy is Cash

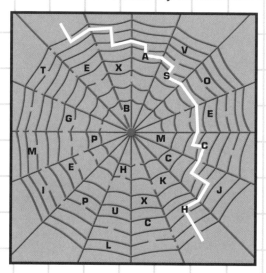

P19 CHROMA-SEARCH

ChromaStone uses lasers

P21 ECHO DUPLICATION

Echo Echo's name is repeated 7 times

P30 CASTLE TRAP!

P38 GLOOPY MAZE!

P40 LASER BLAST-OFF!

Ben should block alien 4.

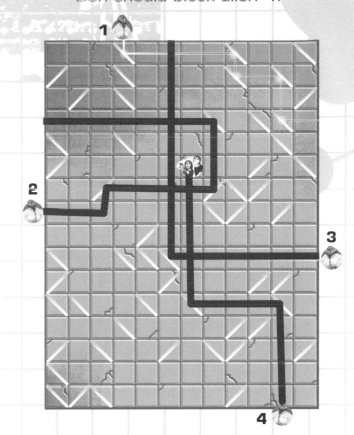

P45 VULKANUS VS KEVIN E. LEVIN

P48 DESTRUCTION

P53 COSMIC SEARCH

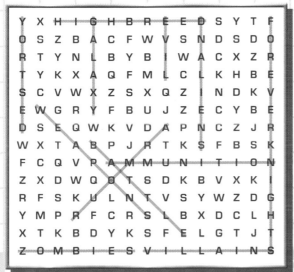

P59 CYBER GRID

NEW BEN 10 ALIEN FORCE STORYBOOKS!

BEN 10 ALIEN FORCE

1
ALL THAT GLITTERS

MAX OUT

2 COOL STORIES ACTION SHOTS INSIDE!

2
PARADOX

PLUMBERS' HELPERS

2 COOL STORIES + ACTION SHOTS INSIDE!

2 COOL STORIES AND AMAZING ACTION SCENE SHOTS...

VISIT THE BEN 10 MICRO-SITE AT
WWW.EGMONT.CO.UK/BEN-10

EGMONT

E0485